HERE'S WHAT KIDS HAVE TO SAY ABOUT THE BOOKS IN THIS EXCITING SERIES:

"I read it practically every day."

"It was fun going on adventures and picking out your own ending . . . It was hard to pick . . . and fun to choose."

"I wouldn't change it in a million billion years."

"It was boring . . . I read it nine times."

"I liked it very very very much."

"It was the best book I ever read."

AND TEACHERS LIKE THE SERIES TOO:

"We have read and re-read, worn thin, loved, loaned, bought for others, donated to school libraries our CHOOSE YOUR OWN ADVEN-TURE book."

"Very original."

"These books really make children think and enjoy it."

CHOOSE YOUR OWN ADVENTURE™

THE CAVE OF TIME

EDWARD PACKARD

ILLUSTRATED BY PAUL GRANGER

BANTAM BOOKS
TORONTO · NEW YORK · LONDON · SYDNEY

RL 4, Age 10 and up

THE CAVE OF TIME

A Bantam Book / July 1979

2nd printing . . . . June 1979	8th printing . . . . October 1980
3rd printing . . . November 1979	9th printing . . . . January 1981
4th printing . . . December 1979	10th printing . . . . April 1981
5th printing . . . . March 1980	11th printing . . . . June 1981
6th printing . . . . May 1980	12th printing . . November 1981
7th printing . . . September 1980	13th printing . . December 1981

This "Choose Your Own Adventure Series" book is based on
"The Adventures of You Series," a Montgomery Associates, Inc.
Trademark for reader participation fiction. Original
conception of Edward Packard.

Illustrations by Paul Granger

ISBN 0-553-20892-6

Published simultaneously in the United States and Canada

Bantam Books are published by Bantam Books, Inc. Its trademark, consisting of the words "Bantam Books" and the por-
trayal of a rooster, is Registered in U.S. Patent and Trademark
Office and in other countries. Marca Registrada. Bantam
Books, Inc., 666 Fifth Avenue, New York, New York 10103.

Printed and bound in Great Britain by
Cox & Wyman Ltd, Reading

The concept, title, and editorial assistance for *The Cave of Time* were provided by Andrea Packard.

THE CAVE
OF TIME

WARNING ! ! ! !

Do not read this book straight through from beginning to end! These pages contain many different adventures you can go on in the Cave of Time. From time to time as you read along, you will be asked to make a choice. Your choice may lead to success or disaster!

The adventures you take are a result of your choice. *You* are responsible because *you* choose! After you make your choice, follow the instructions to see what happens to you next.

Remember—you cannot go back! Think carefully before you make a move! One mistake can be your last . . . or it *may* lead you to fame and fortune!

You've hiked through Snake Canyon once before while visiting your Uncle Howard at Red Creek Ranch, but you never noticed any cave entrance. It looks as though a recent rock slide has uncovered it.

Though the late afternoon sun is striking the opening of the cave, the interior remains in total darkness. You step inside a few feet, trying to get an idea of how big it is. As your eyes become used to the dark, you see what looks like a tunnel ahead, dimly lit by some kind of phosphorescent material on its walls. The tunnel walls are smooth, as if they were shaped by running water. After twenty feet or so, the tunnel curves. You wonder where it leads. You venture in a bit further, but you feel nervous being alone in such a strange place. You turn and hurry out.

A thunderstorm may be coming, judging by how dark it looks outside. Suddenly you realize the sun has long since set, and the landscape is lit only by the pale light of the full moon. You must have fallen asleep and woken up hours later. But then you remember something even more strange. Just last evening, the moon was only a slim crescent in the sky.

You wonder how long you've been in the cave. You are not hungry. You don't feel you have been sleeping. You wonder whether to try to walk back home by moonlight or whether to wait for dawn, rather than risk losing your footing on the steep and rocky trail.

If you decide to start back home, turn to page 4.

If you decide to wait, turn to page 5.

4

As you start walking back toward the ranch, you notice the trail seems very different than you remember it, though of course moonlight can play tricks on your eyes. But you suddenly realize you are not walking on the trail at all, but on what seems to be a dried-up river bed. You hurry back to the cave entrance. You look around you and realize the whole landscape has changed. While you were in the cave, torrents of water have washed out the trail; yet there is not so much as a puddle left. You shiver. It is cold, much colder than it should be at this time of year. You take a jacket out of your backpack and put it on, but you are still freezing.

At least the world about you seems brighter. It's getting light in the east. The sun will soon be up. You look at your watch. It has run down, though you wound it only a few hours ago. Nothing seems to make sense anymore.

You know you should get back to the ranch as quickly as possible; yet somehow you feel the only way to change things back to the way they were is to re-enter the cave.

*If you continue toward the ranch,
turn to page 8.*

*If you go back into the cave,
turn to page 10.*

You wait until morning, but, as the rosy wisps of dawn begin to light the eastern sky, a chill and forbidding wind begins to blow.

If you seek shelter, turn to page 6.

If you brave the freezing wind to see more of the world about you, turn to page 16.

You step into a niche in the rocks to escape the merciless blast of wind and lean back against the rock wall. Suddenly it crumbles under your weight, causing you to fall backward down a muddy slope and into a pond.

The sun shines brightly down on you as you pick yourself up, dripping wet, and wade to the grassy shore. You look back at the rock, rising out of the pond, but you can't see where you fell through.

While you are collecting your senses, a horse comes prancing up, its rider dressed in tin armor—a knight out of the history books— enough to make you laugh. The horseman lifts off his helmet and laughs himself.

"What a place for a bath!" he calls out. "Well, it was worth it—you're cleaner than a pig!" He almost falls off his horse, he is laughing so hard. "But climb on and I'll take you back to the castle," he says. "We'll see if we can't make a human out of you yet."

If you accept the ride back to the castle, turn to page 22.

If you decline the invitation and try to find your way back into the Cave of Time, turn to page 114.

As it gets lighter, you realize you can't be on the right track. The canyon seems shallower than it was. The river bed is strewn with boulders that were never there before. The cold wind chills you to the bone; yet it's the middle of summer. As you climb to higher ground to get a better view, you notice patches of snow. From the top of a ridge you survey a barren plain, frozen lakes, and, in the distance, a massive range of snow-covered mountains. You begin to realize you are not merely lost—you are lost in time, and you have somehow been transported to an Ice Age that occurred many thousands of years ago.

You walk toward one of the cliffs that borders the canyon, seeking shelter from the wind, and notice an entrance to another cave. You are tempted to go inside, but you feel you should keep moving in hopes of somehow reaching familiar country.

If you enter the cave,
turn to page 17.

If you continue on,
turn to page 18.

10

You walk into the interior of the strange cavern; then wait while your eyes become accustomed to the dim, amber light. Gradually you can make out the two tunnels. One curves downward to the right; the other leads upward to the left.

It occurs to you that the one leading down may go to the past and the one leading up may go to the future.

If you take the tunnel leading to the left, turn to page 20.

If you take the tunnel leading to the right, turn to page 61.

If you walk outside the cave again, turn to page 21.

"Off to the tower," the King shouts. Two knights leap forward, drag you out of the chamber, and, with spears at your back, force you to climb forty-eight stone steps to the tower prison—a tiny cylindrical room with one small window looking out over the moat and pasture land beyond. The only furniture is a bed of straw.

You realize you are back in the early days of feudal Europe, where the only laws are the King's whims. You have no idea how long he intends to keep you in the tower. There is one possibility of escape. The water in the moat, about twenty-five feet almost directly below your window, is quite deep. If you jump out far enough, you should land in the deep water and not be hurt.

If you jump, turn to page 12.

If not, turn to page 13.

12

You jump far out and fall faster and faster. You enter the water feet first and hit bottom, but the soft mud receives you gently. In a few seconds you reach the surface. You swim to the outer banks of the moat, shaken but unharmed. You scramble up the bank and run for the cover of the forest.

You walk along the edge of the forest until well out of sight of the castle, then head across the open countryside. You stop a peasant to ask him where you might stay for the night.

"Walk up that hill and you'll see before you the waters of Loch Ness," he says. "You'll find a place there."

You follow his directions and, seeing some little houses near the lake, proceed toward them. Darkness is setting in, and you are glad when you meet a fisherman who says he will give you shelter for the night. He and his wife are kindly people; they invite you to stay and earn your keep by helping them fish.

If you accept, turn to page 66.

If you decide to travel on, turn to page 78.

You decide to wait, but soon regret it. A guard visits you twice a day and brings you only black bread and water. In a few days you feel almost too weak to escape even if you have the chance.

But just as you are beginning to despair of ever regaining your freedom, the guard walks in, smiling.

"The King has ordered you out of here," he says. "We have a much more important prisoner—a man who insulted the King's horse." He laughs in your face. You don't know whether he is telling the truth or not, but he holds the door and waves you out. You walk down the long flight of stone steps to the main courtyard, free again— at least for the moment. The drawbridge is down and there seems to be nothing in the way of your leaving the castle.

There is a splendid black horse tied up near you, probably owned by one of the knights. It occurs to you that you could cover a lot of ground on that horse before anyone realizes what happened.

If you mount the horse and ride off, turn to page 14.

If you ask the King for refuge, turn to page 15.

In a moment you are across the bridge and galloping over the countryside, feeling a good deal smarter than the King and his knights. When you pass some shepherds and wave, they wave back.

You stop to rest at the cottage of a friendly goatherd, who feeds you a good dinner. "Do not fear the King," he says. "He is a fool who sits and drinks grog all day. His only concern is deciding who to put in the tower. His own knights laugh at him, and he is more likely to fall from his throne than you from your horse. Be off now and on to Merrie England, for great things await you there. God speed and good fortune!"

Your energies are renewed by good food and drink, and your horse too is ready to ride. You thank your host warmly and ride off to new adventures and a new life—almost a thousand years before you are born.

The End

You gain entrance to the King and thank him for letting you out of the tower.

"Think nothing of it," the King replies. "We would do as much for any villain. We like your spirit and, though your story makes as much sense as a dancing mule, it brought laughter to our eyes. You have, without meaning it we are sure, performed a service for your King. We thank you.

"We'll see that you have a horse and some pieces of gold," the King continues. "Go and make your fortune. We command you though— come once a year and tell us a story no less amusing than what we have heard from your lips."

"My lord," you say.

"My liege," he replies.

You ride off, somewhat apprehensive, but intent upon making as much of your life as is possible in the year 982.

The End

16

You resolutely trudge along a rocky ridge. It has been cleared of whirling snow by the fierce wind, which bites and blows against your body.

The world seems transformed, and much for the worse. You must find a house or a cabin—people who can help you—or you will die.

As you ponder your fate, you stumble and fall, plunging into a deep crevasse. You black out and later awaken, still shivering, but in a warmer place at least. By the dim amber light, you can see that somehow you have fallen back into one of the chambers in the Cave of Time. A passageway leads to the right, another to the left. Does one lead to the future and one to the past?

*If you enter the left-hand passageway,
turn to page 24.*

*If you enter the right-hand passageway,
turn to page 25.*

As you enter the cave, you see a flickering light ahead and you smell smoke. You make your way along a winding passageway and enter a large chamber. Fires rise out of earthen vessels.

Several short, stocky people with straight black hair and primitive faces are painting pictures on the walls of the cave. They are dressed in animal skins. In a corner of the cave are beds of straw.

You stand, slightly afraid, as the cave people drop their work and run over and stare at you in disbelief. The largest man is carrying a long vine. He steps forward as though he might seize you and tie you up.

If you stay and try to make friends,
turn to page 26.

If you try to run for it,
turn to page 28.

You continue on, following a trail leading up a steep incline. You hear loud, trumpeting sounds from a nearby ravine—the sounds of a large animal. You climb over some rocks and find yourself

looking down on one of the largest land mammals that ever lived—the wooly mammoth. Huge as this creature is, its size is exaggerated even more by its thick coat of wool.

You are cold, desperate, and tired. From your rock ledge, only a few feet over the mammoth, you could drop down on its back, burrow into its warm wool, and ride where it takes you!

If you jump down on the wooly mammoth, turn to page 29.

If you continue on foot, turn to page 30.

The tunnel to the left winds around like a spiral, passing several more tunnels. You turn down one of them, then climb steeply. In a few moments you climb through a hole and emerge in a desert. The weather is extremely hot—certainly over 100 degrees, but the sun is just about to set, so it should be getting cooler. In the distance is a range of mountains, which look extremely high, yet are bare of snow. You have no idea whether you are in the past, the future, or the present. Then you see something that fascinates and disturbs you. The sand seems to be fused into yellowish glass as if heated in a furnace. As you examine the sand more closely, you feel the air getting even hotter. Suddenly you realize the sun is not setting, but rising! The noontime temperature must be more than life can stand. As the sun rises higher, you feel a blistering wave of heat. The light is almost blinding. Could it be that you are witnessing the end of the world?

Turn to page 93.

You turn and walk back out of the cave. It should be dawn by now, but, as you grope your way toward the entrance, you can't see any light coming into the cave. You press against the walls, feeling for an opening. Your hands pass across something cold, wet, and hard. Ice! The entrance is sealed by it. Blocks of ice protrude into the cave.

You step back, feeling confused and helpless. You wish it were just a dream. You retrace your steps a way, trying to think clearly. You know that your only chance to get out of the cave is to follow one of the two branches before you.

If you follow the right branch, turn to page 33.

If you follow the left branch, turn to page 35.

The laughing knight helps you up on his horse and you sit uncomfortably as it canters over the countryside. After traveling a mile or so, you come to a great, stone castle. The horse trots across the drawbridge and into the stable.

"Jump," the knight calls to you, and you slide off the rear of the horse. The knight escorts you into the grand chamber of the castle. All about you are stewards, attendants, and knights. A few minutes later you find yourself bowing before the King himself.

After hearing your story, the King looks gravely at his advisors and knights and stewards. "Does anyone believe this tale?" he asks.

Everyone cries back, "No, Your Majesty," or "Certainly not, Your Majesty."

"Then tell us the truth!" the King roars at you.

If you insist you are telling the truth, turn to page 36.

If you try to make up a plausible story, turn to page 37.

24

You follow the left passageway. It leads upward to the surface. Before you, a grassy meadow slopes down to a clear, fast-flowing stream; beyond it are pine-covered foothills stretching in the distance toward snow-covered peaks. You might be in Wyoming in your own time, but, whatever time it is, the world you see appears to be a hospitable one.

You notice a herd of buffalo grazing. But nowhere can you see a house, or fence, or road, or any sign of human presence. It is possible you are living hundreds, perhaps thousands, of years ago.

You gaze upward. One of the puffy, white cumulus clouds is moving in a strange fashion. It is descending! A spaceship is landing right before your eyes, only a few hundred yards away!

*If you hide from view,
turn to page 38.*

*If you go up to the spaceship,
turn to page 40.*

You walk along the right-hand passageway for a long distance, praying that you can find a tunnel that will lead to your own time. You choose one of the many tunnels you see and follow it. Instead of rising to the surface, you enter a brightly-lighted chamber, in the center of which is a bearded, old man seated in a chair.

"Welcome," he says, as if he has been expecting you.

"Thank you," you reply. "Can you help me find my way back to my own time?"

The old man smiles. "First of all," he says, "tell me why you want to return to your own time instead of another time."

If you say, "Because I want to be back with my family and friends," turn to page 43.

If you say, "Because I don't want to take a chance of being in a bad time," turn to page 41.

If you say, "I would like to try another time, but only if you can assure me that I will eventually get back to my own time," turn to page 44.

If you say, "Who are you?" turn to page 45.

You make friendly gestures. The man holding the vine steps back and smiles. The people talk to you in a friendly fashion, but you cannot understand what they are saying, nor can they understand you. You feel awkward, but happy to be safe and warm for the moment.

Several people have gone back to working on their paintings. You decide to try communicating through drawing. You begin to draw a picture of yourself eating. The cave people laugh, but one of them brings you a slice of half-cooked meat. It

doesn't taste very good, but you are so hungry you don't mind.

Gradually you make friends and learn a few words. Some of the people go hunting and come back with game. Others make clothing from animal skins. You help with cleaning and cooking and each day paint a picture on the walls. The others are fascinated by your drawings of airplanes, ships, and cars—things they see only as abstract designs, for they have no way of knowing what function they could serve.

One day a group of other people visit. You have never seen them before, but your friends welcome them warmly, holding a great feast in their honor. After everyone is through eating, the conversation intensifies. You can tell that the cave people are talking about a serious problem. Then, one by one, they drift off to sleep. You walk outside to see if you can learn anything. The ground is covered with deep snow. A bitter cold wind blows the snow in whirling clouds.

Next morning, the people pack up their belongings and they urge you to do so also. Some migration is obviously intended—no doubt to a warmer climate. You feel you should go with the cave people, but you have a great longing to return to your own home, and your only hope of doing so is to find your way back to the Cave of Time.

*If you go with the cave people,
turn to page 46.*

*If you try to find your way back to
the Cave of Time, turn to page 47.*

28

You can see no future for yourself with these primitive people, so you run back toward the Cave of Time. Fortunately, they do not follow you, and you are able to find your way.

By the time you re-enter the cave, you are hungry and exhausted. The light is dimmer than before and you grope your way along, looking for a passageway. You stumble and fall headfirst down an embankment, bumping your head disagreeably. You look up and see daylight ahead. A minute later, you walk out of the cave into warm, moist air near a forest of leafy trees. A bird flies by. You don't know *when* it is, but it looks pleasant enough.

Turn to page 51.

As you land, the mammoth shudders like a horse shaking off flies. It begins lumbering along up the valley, apparently unaware you are still clinging to its wooly back, keeping warm and enjoying the ride.

The mammoth reaches high ground, nibbles at some bark, and then walks on. Perhaps it will carry you near some cave men who will give you food and shelter.

Suddenly the mammoth stops and turns its head—listening for something. You look up and see human figures approaching from two sides. They are carrying spears and clubs. The mammoth begins to run. You hold on tight. The hunters follow—screaming and yelling. You can't see where the mammoth is heading, but you're afraid the hunters may drive it off a cliff. Yet, if you jump off while it's running, you could be badly hurt.

If you jump to the ground,
turn to page 52.

If you hang on, turn to page 53.

30

Riding on a mammoth might be fun if you were not cold and hungry and lost, but where would it take you? You continue walking, your spirits sinking. Just as you feel ready to sit down and cry, you see an opening in the ground. You crawl in on your hands and knees. It might provide some warmth, and it might lead to the Cave of Time.

You find yourself in a tunnel. There are other tunnels branching off. You feel sure now you are in the Cave of Time. You are eager to take the next tunnel to the surface, but you want to travel a long way forward in time. Maybe you should take a tunnel further on.

If you take the first tunnel that you can, turn to page 54.

If you take a tunnel further on, turn to page 92.

You take the first tunnel and follow it on and on until you begin to wonder whether you are going around in circles. What can this mean? Perhaps time itself is slowing. You are nearing the point of exhaustion, and begin to feel very cold. You see an opening up ahead and stars shining. You step outside on barren ground. It is bitter cold. Even though there is no wind, you know you will freeze if you stay more than a few minutes—maybe not that long, for the air seems very thin, as if you were on top of a very high mountain. You find yourself gasping for breath. You look up at the clear, cold night sky studded with thousands of stars. Among the stars, you notice a disk the size of the sun that gives off a dim red light like a dying ember.

The End

After following the passageway for a considerable distance, you enter a very large tunnel that seems as likely as any to lead you back to your own time. You continue along and soon notice that the floor of the tunnel is becoming sandier. Perhaps you are coming to a beach. Then the sand gives way under your feet; you slide through sand and rising dust. You cannot stop yourself—it is too steep; then there is nothing under your feet, and a moment later you land in deep water. You swim to the surface and catch your breath. You are in an underwater grotto, which seems completely sealed off except for a portion of its roof that is open to the blue sky. You swim to a large, smooth rock sloping into the water.

The sand is white, and the water transparent. The rocks are made of crystalline material of the most delicate shades of blue. For a moment you are overwhelmed by the beauty of the scene before you, but you soon begin to wonder whether you can escape from it. There is no way of climbing out through the opening in the roof.

You dive down in hopes of finding an underwater passageway that might lead to freedom, and you find one! But could you swim through it before running out of air?

If you try to swim through the underwater tunnel, turn to page 58.

If you decide to wait, turn to page 64.

You make your way along in the dim light. Ahead of you is a ladder. You take hold of it and begin to climb. Suddenly you hear a terrible grinding, crunching noise. The ladder shudders. You hold on tight for a few minutes after the noise subsides. Then you continue up the ladder and a moment later pull yourself out into the crisp, cold night air. Lights are glowing all around you. In front of you is a large slab of ice. You feel a strange motion as if the ground is moving. When you touch the ground with your hand, you feel wood. Not far from you is a railing. Beyond it—the sea! Above you are stars more numerous and brilliant than you have seen before. You realize you are on the deck of a very large ship.

Not far from you, hanging on a hook, is an enormous life preserver. Stenciled on it in black letters is the word TITANIC. You know there was only one ship that ever bore that name, that it made only one voyage, that it struck a huge iceberg, and that three hours later it was resting on the bottom of the Atlantic.

As you walk along the deck of the *Titanic,* you realize that below the water line thousands of gallons of water per minute are pouring into the forward compartments. The people don't seem to

Go on to the next page.

realize what's happening. The sea is as calm as glass. The band on the deck below you is playing a waltz. Several men in long black coats and women in fur jackets are walking close by.

"Goodness," one woman says, "I can't understand why the captain has stopped the ship. If we are late docking in New York, I'm going to lodge a complaint with the owners."

If you try to find the captain and warn him that the ship will sink, turn to page 68.

If you go back down the ladder and try to return to the cave, turn to page 79.

You walk along the left-hand passageway, passing tunnels from time to time, none of which looks like a particularly appealing route. You decide to see if you can reach the end of the passageway.

You walk on and on, hour after hour. Then, in the distance, you see a figure approaching—a girl wearing blue jeans and a red sweater and carrying a backpack. She tells you that her name is Louisa and that she was exploring a cave and got lost. She does not know she is in the Cave of Time.

If you try to help Louisa find the way back to where she entered the cave, turn to page 76.

If you suggest she try one of the tunnels with you as a way out, turn to page 80.

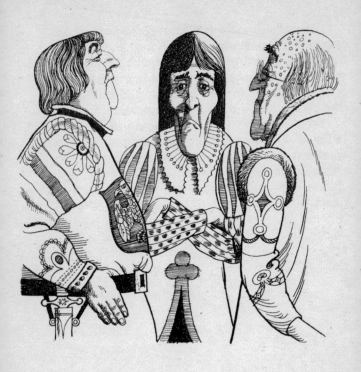

"I know it sounds strange, Your Majesty," you say, "but I have no reason to incur your wrath by making up a false story."

The King looks around at his courtiers. They all have grave expressions on their faces, as if you have committed some unpardonable sin.

Turn to page 11.

"I'm sorry to have intruded upon your royal domain, Your Majesty." you say humbly, trying to think up a good story as fast as you can. "It is true, sire, I have been badly mistreated by my wicked stepfather, with whom I live, and I place myself under your wise and just protection."

"Who is this wicked stepfather and where does he live?" the King asks. "If he is wicked enough, we may want him to be one of our knights," he adds, laughing, as do all the courtiers.

"He lives beyond that hill," you say, pointing toward a high wooded ridge, "and his name is Smith."

The King laughs once again. "Then your stepfather must be a fish," he says, "for beyond yonder hill is Loch Ness."

Turn to page 11.

You feel you must be far in the future. Are you really looking at an alien spaceship? If so, you would rather watch from a safe distance. You climb rapidly up the hill—wondering how you got to this strange time.

Ahead of you is a niche in the rocks. You step inside. You realize you are in the bottom of the crevasse you fell into from the Ice Age. Even if you wanted to get back to that time, there is no way you could do so. You keep walking. Eventually your approach open ground on the opposite side of the hill.

Now you can see a vast stretch of open country—hilly, rocky, and mostly barren. Yet thousands of people are constructing a huge wall! All over the landscape you see oxen pulling carts filled with rocks. The wall is at least twenty feet high and extends as far as the eye can see.

Ladders are strung up against the wall, and on every rung a man or woman is stationed. They hand rocks up one to another to the top of the wall.

You find this sight hardly less amazing than the sight of the alien spaceship, for it appears that you are witnessing the building of the Great Wall of China.

---

*If you go up to the wall builders,
                    turn to page 82.*

*If you return to the crevasse,
                    turn to page 87.*

40

You cautiously approach the spaceship and, to your amazement, see that it is resting a foot or so above the ground, without any visible mechanism keeping it aloft. There are no engines, rocket exhausts, port holes, landing gear, antennae, or any equipment you might imagine a spaceship would need. You realize it must be the product of a supremely advanced civilization.

Trusting that such people have learned to be loving toward others, you approach the ship. A portal slides open, but all you can see within is shimmering blue light. A large cube is thrust out through the portal and lowered to the ground by mechanical arms. The top of the cube is withdrawn, leaving a pallet on which lie the sleeping forms of three men and three women, dressed in shrouds of animal skin. Their bodies and features remind you of pictures you have seen depicting the earliest men on earth. You have an impulse to jump aboard the spaceship before the portal closes.

If you do, turn to page 115.

If not, turn to page 83.

"I can understand," the old man replies, "why you don't want to take a chance with another time, for other times are perilous and filled with evil people and evil deeds.

"You are wise to avoid them, and I will gladly direct you back to your own time, which, you should know, is no better and no worse."

The End

"And why do you want to be back with your family and friends?" the old man asks.

"Because I will miss them and could hardly bear not to see them again. And my family and friends would be sad not to see me."

"You think of others, and you think of yourself too," he replies. "That is a good reason to be in your own time. Take the next tunnel to your right, and you will find your way there. You have chosen to have only one time, have you not?"

"That is true," you reply.

"Then make the most of it," he says, with one hand outstretched to wish you well.

The End

"Ah, you are a shrewd one," the old man says. "You'll try to get two loaves of bread, rather than settle for one. Well, I'll show you one other time, and, if you don't like it, just say so, and I'll return you to your own time, if there is time to do so. Take the tunnel to your left."

You follow his direction, walk through the tunnel, and come out onto a city street. Instantly you realize there is a war going on. Bombs and rockets are exploding all around you. You cry out to the old man, asking to be returned to the Cave of Time, but there is no time left.

The End

"I am a philosopher," the old man says, "who, when asked to choose a time, instead chose timelessness, so that, although nothing would ever happen in my life, I would have all the time in the world to think about it."

"Are you happy with your decision?"

"No, because philosophy is nothing outside of time. Take the tunnel to your right. Return to your own time, and let your life be your philosophy."

The End

Dressed as warmly as possible in your crude boots and coat of animal skins, you leave shortly after sunup with the others, a ragged band of thirty men, women, and children. Luckily there are no babies; they could never survive the migration. The sun shows briefly through the clouds, the wind abates, and you make good progress on your southward journey.

After only a few days of travel, everyone is nearing exhaustion. The hunters have not been able to find enough game. There is no way to light a fire at night and the only way to keep from freezing is to sleep huddled together.

After a week though, you notice the sun shines more warmly at midday and the snow is not quite so deep. It begins to look as though you will survive, though you must give up hope of ever returning to your own time.

The End

You pack up your few belongings. The one you prize most is a knife carved from the tusk of a wooly mammoth. You wave goodbye to your friends and trudge through the snow, trying to retrace your steps back to the Cave of Time. Though the wind is colder than ever, the bright sun stirs your hopes.

You have become much more rugged from living with the cave people, and your crude animal-skin clothes keep you surprisingly warm. You find your way down into the canyon and in a few hours

reach the entrance to the cave, now almost covered with blowing snow.

You are exhausted from the long trek, and your eyes are watering from the cold wind. You hardly notice the large, gray shape only a few yards from the entrance to the cave until you hear the deep, guttural growl of a wolf. Now you stare directly into its cold, cruel eyes. You feel that at your slightest movement it will spring at you. You must think what to do before you move. You probably could outrun the wolf to the cave. It might hesitate before following you—and give you enough time to escape—or you could try to knife the wolf in the throat as it leaps at you.

*If you run for the cave,
turn to page 49.*

*If you prepare to fight,
turn to page 50.*

Slowly you unsheath your knife and then run for the entrance. The wolf is after you like a shot. It leaps and tears your bearskin coat. While the wolf is regaining its balance, you run into the cave and toward the left tunnel. The wolf runs after you. You look over your shoulder and lose your footing. Instead of falling on the ground, you feel yourself sliding down a long, steep chute. Far above, the wolf howls with frustration. You land in a heap at the bottom of a pit—shaken but unharmed. There is a dark passageway to the left. You toss in a stone and, after what seems like a long time, you hear a splash far below. Fortunately, there is another passageway to the right, which is dimly lit by phosphorescent light.

Turn to page 25.

Holding your knife with its long ivory blade pointing upward, you advance very slowly, step by step, toward the wolf, which stands growling softly, apparently confused by your boldness.

Then it springs. You lunge with your knife, twisting your body to avoid its awesome fangs. Your knife cuts through nothing but air, but the wolf succeeds only in tearing off your bearskin coat. It stops for an instant to sniff at the coat, and you turn and plunge your knife into its neck. The wolf twists, looks at you with hate in its eyes, and falls limp, its spinal cord severed.

Now you are a true Stone Age hunter. You skin the wolf and walk into the cave.

You follow the right-hand tunnel, thinking you may find your way back to your own time, but suddenly you feel yourself falling—faster and faster into what seems a bottomless pit.

Turn to page 81.

Suddenly you hear voices shouting. You hide in a thicket. An animal crashes through the brush. In a moment some men rush by in pursuit, carrying spears and slings. You imagine that you must be in an era long before the advent of civilization. You follow an animal trail; it soon leads to a clearing, and you lie down in the grass to rest. Looking up in the sky, you see a long, thin, white streak. You rub your eyes and look again. It seems to be a vapor trail from a jet plane! You may be living in the present time after all.

After several days of wandering through the jungle, you reach a settlement on the banks of a large river. There is an airfield nearby, and within a few weeks you are able to obtain a ride back to civilization and return to your family—just a month after you first entered the Cave of Time. You are happy to be back home, but shocked at how much older everyone looks. And they express the greatest surprise that after eleven years you haven't changed a bit!

The End

You work your way back to the mammoth's rump and slide down, landing hard on the icy ground, where you lie aching and bruised, while the mammoth lumbers on. Suddenly it disappears, driven off the cliff. The hunters are shouting and cheering. Some of them come up to you. They are short and muscular, their jaws jut out, and they have bright squinting eyes. Their black hair hangs down to their shoulders. They are dressed in animal skins.

You look up helplessly, wondering what they will do to you, but in an instant you can see they will not hurt you. They help you up and carry you back to their cave and feed you steaming broth. It tastes awful, but makes you feel much better. You soon learn that the cave people will accept you as one of them, because you have—without realizing it—performed the sacred rite of their culture by riding bravely on the back of a mammoth.

Life is harsh and simple with the cave people, and sometimes you long for your family, your friends, and your own time again; yet your new life is as exciting and happy as you could wish for.

The End

You hold tightly to tufts of wool, hoping the mammoth will slow down enough so you can safely slide off. But suddenly it pitches forward, making a terrible bellowing. In an instant you realize you are falling through space. You cry out helplessly as you lose your grip, falling faster and faster.

Thousands of years later when Dr. Carleton Frisbee, the famous paleontologist, finds your bones next to those of a wooly mammoth in the Red Creek excavation, he is amazed at how closely you resemble a twentieth-century human being.

The End

You enter the next tunnel you come to. It becomes smaller and smaller until you must crawl. You continue this way for almost an hour. Finally, your faith is justified, for you smell a fresh breeze blowing across a field of new-mown hay.

A moment later you are blinking your eyes in the bright sunlight, looking at a beautiful meadow nestled between gentle hills. A dozen or more cows are grazing near a meandering stream. In the distance is a dirt road. A farmer is sitting on a cart filled with hay. A dapple-gray horse is pulling the cart toward a big red barn in the distance. From the other direction you hear the mournful hooting of a train whistle.

You turn around and see that you are only a few hundred feet from the railroad tracks. A train is chugging around the bend, puffs of black smoke rising from its coal-fired steam engine. You are out of the Ice Age, all right, but not exactly in your own time.

Go on to the next page.

The train slows down as it approaches you, and you smile as you see the reason why—a cow is standing on the tracks just ahead, looking as if it would not move for anything. The train pulls to a stop, and a man jumps down from the cab, waving a coal shovel at the cow, which waits almost until the man is upon her before strolling back into the pasture. At that moment you realize you could easily climb onto the back of the train.

If you climb on the train, turn to page 94.

If you go to the farm, turn to page 98.

If you go back into the tunnel in hopes of finding your way back to your own time, turn to page 101.

Through computer instruction you are able to learn the language, which you find is similar to English, so you are soon able to communicate with your hosts.

They are not at all surprised to hear that you arrived through the Cave of Time.

"You are not the first," the head of the household tells you, "but we have visitors from other times only once in a great while. When someone comes, we are always glad to learn about life in another era, because here we have achieved a sort of paradise—we do not work, and the world is at peace. It is a perfect society. That is why primitive epochs, such as yours, interest us so much."

If you stay in "the perfect society,"
turn to page 57.

If you try to return to the Cave of Time,
turn to page 60.

Your hosts give you a fine bedroom with large windows overlooking the park on one side. On another wall is a beautiful painting of the California seacoast. When you push a button, the painting folds up to the ceiling, revealing a large screen. Your room contains a computer terminal that enables you to select any movie or other program you desire from over 10,000 possibilities. There are even films where *you* are the main character and *you* can make choices as to what will happen next in the story. Then, if you don't like the way the plot is working out, *you* can go back to an earlier point and make different choices from then on.

On your terminal you can also play games and flash pages of books or magazines on the screen. You can live quite well without even getting out of bed.

Eventually you go exploring. You meet other people, but you find none of them very interesting, so you spend most of your time watching the greatest movies of all time. Gradually you settle into your new life. One thing disturbs you. No one has made any new movies in the last 300 years.

The End

You take a deep breath, dive down, and swim through the tunnel. There is light ahead. In a moment you surface in a beautiful lagoon. Thatched cottages are nestled among the palm trees that rim the white sand beach. A warm, soft breeze brings the scent of jasmine and the sound of strange melodies from sonorous drums. Looking out to the inlet from the sea, you can see a fleet of outrigger skiffs with multi-colored sails running into the lagoons before the wind, their owners leaning against the booms to hold the sails out.

You walk toward the village. Several handsome, brown-skinned people see you. Some of them run away, but others walk toward you with hands held up in salute. Two children, holding garlands of flowers, run up to you. Someone calls—"Aloha!"

Soon you are sitting in front of a huge beach fire, cooking crabs and eating buana cake. Having never had a visitor before, your hosts are happy to see you. They welcome you into their society. Gradually you learn their language. The boys tell you they are your brothers; the girls that they are your sisters.

You enjoy life in this new paradise, but you still wonder whether there might be a way to get back

to the Cave of Time. Your new friends are unable to help. Perhaps if you journeyed inland you could find some who could. Your friends warn you against trying, however. They tell you that you will find only terrible jungles and rivers filled with crocodiles.

If you remain with your new friends, turn to page 62.

If you journey inland, turn to page 63.

There is something deadening about the perfect future society that makes you want to return to your own time as quickly as possible. With a brief word of farewell, you hurry back to the tunnel, climb down, and find a fork to the right that you hope will take you toward the right time. Soon you are climbing up toward the surface, excited about the discovery you are about to make.

When you reach the surface, it is completely dark. A chill wind is blowing. You sit resolutely waiting for dawn so that you can see what kind of a world you are in. Meanwhile, there is no way of telling what time it is, either by your watch or by the stars.

You hear loud, clicking sounds all around you, mostly in the distance, but some quite close. As the orange-pink glow of oncoming dawn lightens the eastern sky, you see nearby the shape of a creature that is the size of a sheep but has a very different appearance.

The End

You follow the tunnel downward a short distance, suddenly you are sliding. Your head strikes something and you are knocked unconscious.

When you wake up, you find yourself by a small lake, bordered by woods. A boy about twelve years old is fishing nearby, but there is no one else in sight. You go up and introduce yourself, hoping you can find out what year it is without sounding crazy.

Fortunately, the boy is friendly and good natured. He tells you his name is Nick Tyler and that he lives on Birch Street. He works in his father's business making candles and soap—the best in the Colonies, he says.

If you tell him you come from a future time, turn to page 104.

If you try to make up a believable story, turn to page 106.

Your friends are understanding about your wish to find the way back to your own time, but they tell you they can show you something you never dreamed of. Since their society is very primitive, you wonder what they could have in mind.

Next day they lead you to another cove where the waves roll in, rise up against the cliff and then roll out again. Sometimes the waves clap against each other and send a foamy spray of water high in the air. You see some young people on tiny rafts—nothing more than surfboards—riding in on the crests of the waves and then riding them out on the rebound. In a few hours you have learned a sport that brings excitement and fascination for hour after hour.

With such delights as this, it is not long before you lose interest in returning to your own time. Sometimes you wonder, but you never learn, whether this paradise lies in the future or the past.

The End

You hug your friends good-bye and climb the ridge bordering the jungle. You soon find an animal trail leading through the dense undergrowth into a tropical rain forest. The green canopy of treetops is far overhead and only an occasional dapple of sunlight reaches the spongy, dark ground. You walk on and on, hoping to reach the mountains, where you might find another entrance to the Cave of Time.

Night falls and you make yourself a crude bed. Your mattress is the mossy floor of the forest. You spread out fern leaves for a sheet. Early the next morning, as the birds are beginning their morning songs, you are awakened by the boa constrictor wrapped around your neck.

The End

Swimming through the underwater tunnel may be the only way to get out of the grotto, but the risk of drowning seems too great. You explore the rocks in the grotto and think about how you might possibly get up through the roof.

Suddenly a voice calls, "Hello." You whirl around and notice for the first time, huddled in the corner, a woman with sparkling blue eyes and a mysterious smile. She is sitting crosslegged, propped against a rock which is shaped in a way that gives her a comfortable seat. In her hands she is holding a flute, and as you stare in amazement she plays an unfamiliar melody with a sweetness and purity of tone such as you have never heard.

"Hello," you reply. "Tell me—who are you and how can we get out of here?"

"Sit down," she says, "and relax. You have all the time in the world."

"What do you mean?" you reply. "I am trapped. I slid down from the Cave of Time and I want to get out."

"Believe me," the woman says, "there's no way

to get out; but do not be concerned. It is a beautiful place and you can be very happy here."

"But we'll starve. How long have you been here?" you exclaim.

"Forever and not at all," she replies, "for this is the part of the cave which leads neither to the past nor to the future. Here, time does not exist, so, of course, you will never be hungry or bored, and, although you can never get out, you will be here for no time at all."

Turn to page 102.

You accept the offer, for you can hardly expect a better life at this point, and soon you begin to enjoy rowing out in the early morning mists and spreading your nets with the neighboring fishermen.

One afternoon, as the people are pulling up their boats for the night, your friend, Angus McPhee, raises a cry and points at the water. You look out and see the great head and neck of a sea monster—a huge dragon of the lake. Nearby, splinters of wood are floating in the water.

"That was Sutherland's boat," Angus cries out. "It's been a hundred years since the monster has been seen, but now it has returned!"

The monster swims away and soon is lost from view in the mists.

"How could the monster be gone for a hundred years and then return?" you ask Angus.

"Somewhere near Beatty's Point," he replies, "there is an underwater cave where the monster stays as long as it pleases—because it is a Cave of Time."

If only you could find your way back to the Cave of Time! But chances seem slim, and the risks seem great.

If you try, turn to page 70.

If you do not try, turn to page 74.

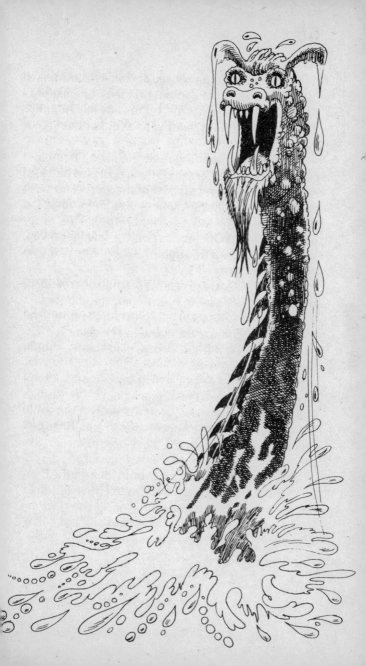

Could you change history and save hundreds of lives by warning the captain that the "unsinkable" *Titanic* is destined for the bottom of the Atlantic? You see some stairs leading to a higher deck, and you run up them.

A steward is standing near the top. "You can't come up here," he cries. But you dart past him and run toward the forward part of the ship. You dash up another set of stairs, where you find yourself at the starboard wing of the bridge. The gray-bearded captain is standing only a few feet away, looking out to sea through his binoculars at a ship on the horizon.

"Captain," you call out. "You may not realize it, but this ship will sink in only two or three hours."

He turns and looks at you gravely. "I know," he says softly. "But we are going to fire distress rockets. That ship out there—the *Californian*—should respond to help us."

"They will not respond, Captain," you tell him. "They can't believe the *Titanic* could be in trouble, even though they see your rockets. Your only hope is to put your strongest men in a lifeboat and have them row toward the *Californian* at top speed—firing rockets as they approach."

"Great heavens, you have bold ideas," the captain replies, "but I need every man I have to lower our lifeboats and keep order among the passengers. I can't believe the *Californian* will not come when they see our rockets.

"Now go to the deck below. Mr. Lightoller will see that you have a place in a lifeboat."

With that the captain turns and strides away, giving orders to an officer nearby. You sadly return down the stairs and wait in line for one of the places in a lifeboat.

Two hours later, you sit huddled in the crowded boat, shivering in the cold breeze, and watch the great *Titanic* slip beneath the waves—with 1,500 people still aboard—together with your only hope of finding your way back to the Cave of Time.

The End

One day when the sun is bright and the water as warm as it's likely to get, you take an old skiff and row to Beatty's Point. You pull your boat up on the rocky shoal that marks the cave. You dive again and again along the rock wall that drops into the depths until you find the entrance. You swim a few feet inside and find you can get up to the surface inside an enormous cavern, most of it filled by an underground lake.

You reach the shore and walk along the lakeside, deeper and deeper into the cavern, which is lit by a mysterious blue light. Then, ahead, you see what you had hoped to find—a tunnel that surely must lead to the Cave of Time. Nearby in the sand are three eggs as large as footballs. You pick one up and carry it into the tunnel. After walking awhile, the air becomes hard to breathe. You begin to feel dizzy and fall unconscious to the ground, still clutching the enormous egg.

Go on to the next page.

You are awakened by a fresh breeze blowing toward you. You dizzily get to your feet, pick up the egg, and hurry toward the fresh air—outdoors again in Snake Canyon! Everything is as you remember it and in a few hours you are walking up to the ranch, where your uncle says he is surprised you got back so quickly!

When you tell what has happened to you, no one at the ranch believes it, though they are fascinated by your enormous egg.

"Maybe we'll believe that egg is real—and believe your story—if it will hatch a monster," your uncle says, "or if you break it open to show us what's inside."

If you decide to break the egg open, turn to page 72.

If you keep it in your closet until you have a chance to get scientific advice, turn to page 103.

With your aunt and uncle and some ranch hands standing by, you very gently tap the egg with an axe, hoping it will split open without fragmenting.

"Wait a minute!" Uncle Howard cries out. "I'm ready to believe you, but I think we better get a naturalist down from the University to see this first."

You are relieved that your uncle feels this way, because it seems like a terrible responsibility—cracking open an egg like that and possibly killing a rare monster before it is born.

Uncle Howard calls the naturalist, a famous professor of paleontology, who agrees to come down the following Saturday. You place the egg in a large bowl in the middle of the dining room table.

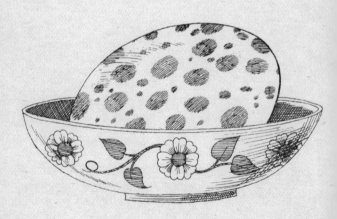

The next day is Friday, and that evening the whole family goes out to the movies. When you return, you find the house has been broken into and the egg is missing.

Neither you, your aunt and uncle, nor any of the ranch hands, nor the police are ever able to find the egg. Most people you tell your story to just smile and say, "Sure." But Uncle Howard, even though he is a skeptical man, tells you he knows you were telling the truth.

The End

The idea that the Loch Ness monster goes into the Cave of Time for a hundred years or so before returning seems preposterous. And, even if it does, it seems very doubtful you could dive down deep enough to find the underwater entrance. So you resign yourself to making a living fishing the waters of Loch Ness.

You find it a tolerable, though not very interesting, life. You particularly like rowing out in your skiff in the early morning mists and watching the pale, red sun struggling to shine through the haze. That's what you are doing one day when you feel a tremendous thump under your boat, the stern is heaved high into the air, and you are hurled over the bow and into the jaws of the monster.

Some of your friends find the wreckage of your boat later in the day and, throughout the village, people say to each other—"The monster has returned again."

The End

After hearing of the forbidding world you've witnessed at *your* end of the Cave of Time, Louisa is agreeable to your helping her try to find the way back to her entrance.

"Tell me about the world outside your entrance to the Cave of Time. Is it in America? What year is it there?" you ask, as the two of you walk along.

"The year 2022, of course," she replies.

"You mean people are still wearing blue jeans then?" you ask.

"They've come back into style lately," she laughs.

"You must have some new inventions that we did not have in my time. Tell me about your most modern things."

"I think the best things are the bicycle trails. Since 1997 they've allowed no new roads to be built—only bike trials—and now there are as many miles of bike trails as there are of roads for cars.

"So you can really bike all over the country?" you ask.

"Sure—and not alongside buses and trucks and crazy drivers, but through forests and across plains and deserts and along rivers and streams. I sometimes feel like biking forever that way, and there are hostels for bikers where you can sleep in comfort for almost nothing. Most of the cost is paid for by taxes on gasoline."

Suddenly you feel the ground giving way beneath your feet. You and Louisa are falling. The two of you land at the base of a steep bluff, shaken but unharmed, alongside a road. You wonder what year you have arrived in. Then, nearby, you see a billboard that says, "CADILLAC—the Car of the Year, every Year!"

"What's a Cadillac?" Louisa asks.

The End

You'd rather spend the rest of your life searching for an entrance to the Cave of Time than settle for the placid life of a fishing village. So you bid your new friends farewell and set out over the countryside, headed south for London. Your goal is to find a ship to take you to America, though you know America hasn't been discovered yet, for somehow you must find your way back to Red Creek Canyon and the Cave of Time.

A few hours later, as you are walking on a road along the edge of the forest, some burly men ride out from behind a clump of trees.

"We've got you," one shouts. "You're the one who escaped from the tower, aren't you?" They force you upon a horse and ride at top speed toward the castle.

"The penalty for escaping from the tower is hanging," one of them tells you.

You find out he is right.

The End

You have no wish to risk sinking with the *Titanic*, so you climb back down the ladder into the hold of the ship—hoping that somehow you will find your way back to the cave. In your haste, you lose your grip and fall. You reach out, but too late. You land so hard you are knocked out. When you awaken, you are in one of the passageways of the cave.

If you explore the passageway, turn to page 86.

If you decide to check out the outer entrance to the cave again, turn to page 88.

"Since you can't find your way to your own time," you say, "perhaps we can find my time." You lead her back a short distance, until you come to an unusually wide tunnel. You stop, and Louisa looks at you inquiringly. "Let's try this one," you say.

After traveling almost an hour, the two of you smile with joy to ee light ahead, and you soon come out of the tunnel and stand on reddish sandy ground, surveying a saucer-shaped terrain. The air is as fresh and clear as on a crisp, fall day. You guess that you may be in the crater of an extinct volicano. Suddenly, there is a thundering roar behind you. Louisa and you run from a landslide that buries the tunnel leading back to the Cave of Time.

"I wonder what year it is?" Louisa asks, after the two of you have collected your wits.

For the first time you look up at the sun. It is four times as large as the sun you knew, though not as bright. It is almost directly overhead, yet its color is a rusty red.

"I don't know the answer," you reply, "but from what I've read about astronomy, I would guess it's the year 2,000—plus about four billion years."

The End

You feel yourself slowly regaining consciousness. You are in your bed at Red Creek Ranch, looking up at Uncle Howard. Standing nearby is a friend of his who is a doctor.

"You took quite a bad fall climbing on those rocks up in the canyon," Uncle Howard says. "Doc Parsons tells me he doesn't know why you didn't break any bones. We were real worried about you—thought you got lost in one of those caves up there."

You feel a bit dizzy and weak, so you just smile and say nothing. Probably no one would believe you anyway. Years later, though, you write a book about your adventures in the Cave of Time.

The End

You go up to the base of the wall where the people are working. When they see you, they imagine you are a spy from some unknown tribe. Some guards capture you and force you to sit on a pile of rocks while they talk about you.

After a while they point to one of the ladders. Two other people force you to start handing up rocks. You realize that you have been conscripted to work building a wall twenty feet high, twelve feet wide, and 1,400 miles long. You calculate it will take about ten billion rocks to build the wall. You wonder how many of them you will lift before you can escape—if you ever do.

The End

Much as you would like to see the inside of the alien ship, you have no desire to be whisked off into space. You step back to what you hope is a safe distance and watch what happens. In a moment the portal closes, and almost instantly the ship rises, silently, straight up. Within a few minutes it is lost from view. You walk over to look more closely at the primitive looking people sleeping on the pallet. They begin to stir and stretch and rub their eyes as if waking from a long sleep.

If you stay and try to make friends with the primitive people, turn to page 85.

If you return to the hill and try to find your way back to the Cave of Time, turn to page 84.

84

You run up the hill and out of sight before any of the primitive people awaken. You must find an entrance to the Cave of Time. You search in the high rocky ground for some opening. Hours go by; dusk is fast approaching. Just as you are about to give up hope, you spy the entrance to a cave under a rock ledge. You eagerly step inside and have only a moment's awareness that it is the den of a saber-toothed tiger.

The End

The people look around curiously. They hardly seem to notice your presence. One by one they get up and walk around. One of them drinks from the stream. They make grunting and clicking noises, but do not seem to be actually talking among themselves. The largest of the group picks up a stick from the ground and begins prying up the roots of plants along the edge of the stream. He bites at each one. Finally he smiles and passes the root around to the others. One woman claps her hands. The others begin to find sticks. One of the men hands you a piece of root. You bite at it. It tastes like a dirty carrot. The women smile at you. You are accepted in the group.

The next morning you wake up in the soft mossy bank in Snake Cavern, a few dozen yards from the entrance to the cave, wondering how much of what has been happening to you has been a dream and how much has been reality. But you have no desire to go into the Cave of Time again.

The End

You walk on and on, hoping the passageway will lead you to your own time. You soon come to a tunnel that leads into a dark, musty room resembling the cellar of a large house. There are a great many people huddled in groups, sitting on blankets in complete darkness save for the light of a few flickering candles. You hear the dismal wail of a siren. Near the center of the room an old-fashioned radio sits on the table playing a mixture of classical music and static. Then the sirens stop, the ground shakes, and you hear a tremendous explosion nearby, then another further away, then another so close that a wall and half the ceiling come crashing down in a pile of rubble, blocking the tunnel. You and the others scramble to the opposite side of the room, coughing and gasping in the dust-filled air.

You are about to begin a new life. The year is 1940; the place, London.

The End

You have no desire to be involved in building the Great Wall of China, or, for that matter, to be taken to another planet by aliens. You walk back into the crevasse, hoping to find a tunnel that might lead to another time. You walk along the bottom of the crevasse and reach an opening on the other side of the ridge, where you half expect to see the rolling countryside, the stream and the space ship that were there before.

Instead, the crevasse leads to the ocean! Like a bad dream, where the scene suddenly changes into something entirely different, you find that the hills have become waves, which surround you so that the rock you are standing on is only a reef protruding a few yards above the wind-swept seas. And there seems to be no escape, because, for all you can tell, you are standing on the only land in the world.

The End

You walk back through the cavern, wondering if the entrance will still be blocked by ice. This time, though, you are greeted by a warm breeze. Sunlight is shining on the ground near the entrance, and you walk outside.

Squinting your eyes in the bright light, you see a world totally different from the one you know. You are on a hillside. For miles and miles you can see grassy plains speckled with lakes. Nearby is a forest of towering ferns, swaying in the wind. The world before you seems strangely quiet, except for the faint rumbling of distant thunder. Suddenly, the thunder seems much closer—and louder. The thundering sound is moving through the ferns. You run up the hill looking for a place to hide. A huge shadow passes on the ground. Above you, soaring through the air, is a creature larger than any bird you have seen.

Go on to the next page.

Now it is clear what has been happening. The cave is a crack in the universe—a place outside space-time. Once inside its tunnels you could find yourself at any place, at any time. If you enter again you might be sent to a place from which you could never escape. Yet that is your only hope of returning to your own place and time.

If you go back into the cave, turn to page 90.

If you remain outside, turn to page 91.

Inside the cave again, you feel depressed and confused. Your eyes do not seem to be getting used to the dim light. You cannot find any passageways leading to other times. You feel increasingly drowsy. Soon you fall asleep on the cold clay floor of the cave.

Sometime later you awaken. The cave is pitch dark, but the bright light at the opening tells you the sun is shining brightly outside. You walk out into the daylight and, to your surprise and delight, you see Snake Canyon, the trail, the grove of pine trees nearby—everything just as it was when you entered the cave. Even the sun is in the same place, just about to pass behind the rim of the canyon. Somehow you have returned to your own time—or more precisely, the time it was before you fell asleep in the cave.

You rub your eyes and start down the path back to the Red Creek Ranch with a story to tell that no one will believe, but that you will never forget.

The End

Reasoning that you can always find your way back into the cave when you want to, you decide to explore the world in which you have found yourself.

You make your way along a rock ledge overlooking the plains and lakes, taking care to keep your bearings so you can find your way back to the cave.

By now you are getting very hungry. You know that you are in the age of reptiles—at least 100 million years ago—and that mammals may not yet have appeared on earth. There will be no rabbits or deer to hunt, though the lakes may contain fish. You wonder how dinosaur eggs taste.

You follow a wide path through the fern trees. When you round the first bend, you find yourself face to face with the horrible Triceratops, a great gray monster almost hidden behind its shields and horns. It looks at you curiously with dull brown eyes. You turn, run, and crash into a tree trunk— one that wasn't there before!

The bark feels like leather. You look up to see how high it is—into the jaws of Tyrannosaurus Rex.

The End

You continue a long distance until you come to the next tunnel. From there it is only a short distance until you reach the surface. An amazing sight meets your eyes.

As far as you can see, the land looks like a beautiful park, with soft, feathery grass and towering trees. Here and there are clusters of multicolored, dome-shaped buildings, connected by ramps, terraces and walkways. Some people dressed in simple khaki pants and shirts and tan sneakers walk up to you. They do not understand your language, nor you theirs. They look much like the people of your time except that they are unusually trim, muscular, and healthy looking, and they are a good deal smaller than your own people.

They take you inside a dome-shaped building and show you electronic equipment that looks like a computer. You notice a typewriter, so you sit at it and type a message.

The computer prints out a reply. It apparently has access to memory banks containing your language. You soon discover you are living in the year 3742.

Turn to page 56.

You dive down into the tunnel, hoping you can make it back to an earlier time. Gratefully, you feel cool, damp air coming up from the cave. You are curious to try the next tunnel you come to, thinking that it may show the state of the world just before it began to burn up from the intensifying heat of the dying sun, or that it might show what happened afterward! But you suspect that a tunnel further on might be more likely to lead you back to your own time.

If you take the first tunnel, turn to page 31.

If you take a tunnel further along the way, turn to page 32.

You climb up the steps between the last car and the caboose just as the train begins to start up again. When you open the door to the car, you are surprised to see soldiers in blue uniforms holding old-fashioned rifles. They advance upon you. One of them strides past you to see if anyone else followed you.

"How did you know this was the President's car?" the first soldier asks you.

"What President?" you reply.

Then, to your amazement, you get the answer to your question, for the very tall bearded man walking down the aisle could be no one else but Abraham Lincoln.

"That's all right," the President tells the soldiers, "I could use some company right now. You may stay until we reach Gettysburg," he says to you. "But maybe you should get off at Parkersville. I know of some good people there who will help you out."

If you stay on until Gettysburg,
turn to page 96.

If you get off at Parkersville,
turn to page 100.

"I'd like to stay on till Gettysburg," you say.

"Well, that's fine," the President replies. "Why don't you sit across from me? I have to write out a little talk I'm giving there, and, while I'm doing that, you think about what you're going to make of your life, because you can't spend all your time riding on trains, after all."

You nod in agreement and sit quietly watching the President scribbling some lines on an envelope. After awhile he looks up from his writing and you look each other in the eyes.

"You have a great future," he says abruptly.

"How can you tell," you ask.

"By looking at your face."

"Just by that?"

"Just so."

As you are talking, you notice two elaborately dressed men approaching from the end of the car. They whisper a few words to the President. He excuses himself, shakes hands with you, and tells one of his soldiers to see that you are provided for in Gettysburg.

Go on to the next page.

When you arrive at Gettysburg, one of the soldiers takes you to a family who welcomes you warmly and agrees to put you up for awhile, if you will help them out with their farm.

You find it amazing to be living in a time with no cars, radios, television, record players, or even telephones. It's peaceful—at least when there is not a war going on—but you feel homesick. You feel the great future the President predicted for you lies in your own time, and you resolve to find your way back to the Cave of Time.

The End

If you take the train, it may ruin your chance to return to the Cave of Time. It seems best to stay close to the tunnel. At any rate, you decide you will be able to think better after getting something to eat, so you walk over to the farmhouse.

The farmer's wife gives you a bowl of soup, but she won't believe the story you make up to explain your presence there. You soon get the idea you are not welcome, so you trudge on into town, where the innkeeper lets you have a room for the night.

The next morning you get a ride on a coach to Philadelphia. A Quaker family takes you in and helps you get work as a carpenter's apprentice. You don't like the job, and soon you leave

Philadelphia to go to New York, where you are able to find a job working for a newspaper. Eventually you travel all over the world. You live a long and wonderful life, dying just a few years before you are born.

The End

It's less than a mile to Parkersville, and the President shakes your hand and wishes you luck. One of the soldiers arranges with the station agent for a carriage to take you to a farm owned by an old friend of his.

You soon become a member of the family. They are good people and make you feel very much at home. You are surprised to learn, however, that they plan to sell their farm and move to California. The new life in the West they describe is so appealing that you decide to go with them.

You never regret it, except, sometimes, you wish you could see your own time again.

The End

With considerable trepidation you slide down the tunnel. You mean to turn off at one of the side passageways that might take you back to your own time, but you are too exhausted to search for the entrance. You half slide, half climb down the tunnel—further back into time—then you lose your balance. You fall a great distance, land in deep water, and sink a long ways.

You are barely able to surface and, when you do, you find that the air is filled with dense fog. The water is warm, but the fog is so thick you can hardly breathe. The air smells slightly of sulphur. Gasping for breath, you realize you must be several billion years in the past and that oxygen has not yet been released into the atmosphere.

The End

You sit down and rest your chin in your hands, unable to believe the fate that has befallen you. To live forever in a timeless world seems worse than death.

"Well, to tell the truth, there is a way to get back to your own time," the woman finally says, "but, if you follow it, you will not be able to live forever."

"I don't care," you say. "Show me the way."

"Very well," she says, shaking her head in disbelief. "Dive under the rock ledge beneath me and swim through the tunnel you will find there. You will come up in your own time. Don't worry, it's only a few yards. You can make it."

You take a last look around, wave good-bye and dive. A few seconds later you surface in a pond just inside the entrance of the Cave of Time. You swim to shore and run out through the cave entrance into the open air, almost crashing into your Uncle Howard, who has come looking for you.

"You're late for dinner," he says. "We wondered what happened to you. You ought to keep better track of the time."

The End

The next day you call the Department of Zoology at a nearby university, where you are referred to Dr. Henry Karn, a specialist in large reptiles. Dr. Karn is skeptical about the egg but agrees to drive to Red Creek Ranch immediately to see it.

By the time he arrives, you are feeling very nervous. Suppose the egg is just made of plastic? Your concern is heightened by his stern appearance. He shakes hands brusquely with you and your uncle and immediately asks to see the egg.

When you hand it to him, he says nothing while he stares intently at it, holds it up to the light, taps it and scratches it with a pen knife. Then he holds it to his ear.

Finally he smiles at you and gently puts the egg down. "It's quite possible this is the egg of a Plesiosaurus, an aquatic dinosaur of the late Jurassic period. It is highly unlikely it will ever hatch. Even so, I would want to keep it in an incubator at the University for at least a year before breaking it open. I'll let you know, of course, if anything develops."

A few weeks have passed since then and whenever the phone rings you wonder if Dr. Karn is calling.

The End

When you tell him you come from the Twentieth Century through the Cave of Time, Nick smiles. Then you tell him a little about life in your own time—about cars and planes, telephones and television. He listens intently, with a big grin on his face, as if you are telling th funniest story ever told.

"I'm so glad to meet you," Nick says. "I've always wanted to know about life in the Twentieth Century." He tries to look serious, but begins to laugh, thinking it's all a joke.

"Seriously," you say, (since you know he will never believe you) "I have no home. Do you know of a place where I can stay?"

"I'm sure you can stay at our house," he says warmly. "We have such a big family, one more won't matter, but you must be willing to work in the shop with the rest of us."

Since you feel you hardly have any other choice, you accept his offer and feel grateful when his parents give you a good dinner and a comfortable bed. Nick tells you, with much seriousness, that you are living in the year 1718 in Boston, the principal town in the British colony of Massachusetts.

You soon become one of the family. They are good people and treat you well. But each day you have to work long hours boiling soap and pouring it into molds, waiting on customers and doing errands for Nick's father, whom you have come to know as Uncle Ted.

Your neighbor, Mr. Nelson, is a printer. He recently returned from England with a printing press and letter type he bought there. The business interests you, and you consider working as his apprentice, but to do so you would have to sign papers indenturing yourself to work faithfully for him for six full years.

If you decide to stay at home and continue to work for Uncle Ted, turn to page 107.

If you decide to be indentured to be an apprentice in Mr. Nelson's printing business, turn to page 109.

You do your best to make up a story about how you ran away from home, but Nick sees that you are not telling him the truth. While you're talking, he packs up his fishing gear, says goodbye, and walks off.

Once he is out of sight, you start down the road and, after a mile or so, reach a settled area. While you are standing near a church, wondering what to do next, a constable approaches and asks where you're from. This time you try to explain what *really* happened. After listening awhile, he arrests you for disorderly conduct and locks you up in the local jail.

Later in the day, a big, stupid-looking guard comes to bring you a ration of soup and bread. He is fascinated by your strange clothes and by the rumors he has heard about you. After opening the door to your cell, he hands you your food and stands back and looks at you curiously.

"They say you're in league with the devil," he says. "Is it so?"

If you try to run past the guard and escape, turn to page 111.

If you tell him you are innocent, turn to page 113.

Although you feel you would probably enjoy the printing business more than a career as a soap maker, you wish to remain free to take advantage of some other opportunity.

The work with Uncle Ted is tedious. You feel you could not bear life devoted to making candles and soap. You spend most of your spare time reading what books you can lay hold of, but you are anxious to travel and see the world.

Not long afterwards, you sign up on the brigantine, *Nina,* as a deck hand. The ship is owned by a rich merchant, and it is bound for Barbados in the West Indies with a load of lumber and then on to England.

You find life at sea much harder than you expected, especially when you are required to climb the rigging in a howling gale, but eventually you become captain of your own ship. In every place you visit you ask the people you meet whether they have ever heard of the Cave of Time.

The End

You go to work in Mr. Nelson's shop and soon become proficient in the art of printing. But after awhile, you become increasingly unhappy. Mr. Nelson refuses to raise your wages or give you a chance to own part of the business. There are no jobs available for you in Boston, so you decide to move to Philadelphia, where you have heard there is a greater demand for printing.

Happily, Mr. Nelson agrees to release you from your indenture, and by selling almost all your possessions, you are able to raise enough money to engage passage on a coastal schooner. After a long and stormy voyage down the coast, your ship docks early on a Sunday morning at the Market Street wharf in Philadelphia.

You are tired and hungry and you use some of your last money to buy a loaf of bread. Out of curiosity, you follow some well-dressed people into the Quaker meeting house. The people seat themselves, but, following custom, no one speaks. It is so peaceful you fall sound asleep. When you awaken, the Quakers welcome you. One family gives you lodging and, fortunately, you are able to get a job with one of the two printers in the town.

Go on to the next page.

You work hard to improve your skills as a printer. Within a few years, with the help of some friends, you are able to raise enough money to go into business on your own.

Your printing business thrives, and after awhile you start your own newspaper. It begins to look as if the Eighteenth Century is a pretty good time for you to be alive.

The End

The guard is too startled, and maybe even too afraid, to stop you as you dart past him and out of the jail house. You run down the street as fast as you can. As you stop to catch your breath, a thin, bearded man driving a coach pulls up next to you.

"You seem to be in some trouble," he calls out. "Can I be of help?"

Too tired to make up any story, you begin to tell him everything that has happened to you. He is very excited by your story and invites you to a nearby tavern, where you have your first good meal since you left Red Creek ranch. Your host hardly eats anything. He looks pale and seems to have a bad cough.

Go on to the next page.

When you finish recounting your tale, he says, "It is strange that we have met. I have tuberculosis, and no doctor in Boston can help me. My only hope is to reach a future time."

"I think it's my only hope too," you say.

"If we help each other, I think we can find our way back to your time—my new time," he replies.

The two of you shake hands on it and set out on your quest the next day at sunrise.

Together, you are successful in finding your way to the present time. Your friend from the past is cured with the help of modern medicines and later becomes a history teacher who is known throughout the country for his amazing knowledge of life in colonial America.

The End

When you tell the guard you are innocent, he scowls and slams shut the door of the cell. "You'll not take me to the devil with you!" he calls back as he walks away.

The next day you are brought into a courtroom before a stern looking judge. After hearing the charges against you and listening to what you have to say, he shakes his head and scowls angrily. Then he looks at the prosecutor and pounds his fist on the bench.

"Your charge against this person is for disorderly conduct, but the specifications you give are 'strange clothes and telling stories invented by the devil.' What you really are charging is witchcraft! There will be no such madness in my court and let me have none of it again from you! Case dismissed."

The judge not only sets you free, but afterwards gives you a home to live in and helps you on your way to a good and happy life in the Eighteenth Century.

The End

There is a certain tone in the knight's laughter that does not inspire your trust, so you thank him graciously and tell him you have other business to attend to.

"Then go to it," the knight replies. "Take care to keep your business drier than yourself!"

He gallops off in a rush. You are glad to be rid of him.

Eager to find the entrance to the Cave of Time, you climb up behind the rock wall that slopes into the pond. After searching for an hour, you find a tunnel leading underground.

Turn to page 61.

You jump aboard and find yourself in a sealed chamber. The walls surrounding you remind you of the inside of a bathtub. It occurs to you that the beings who control this spaceship have some means of manipulating time. Could it be that the Cave of Time is their creation? As you are thinking these thoughts, you become increasingly drowsy. In a moment you are asleep.

You awaken in darkness, wondering if you may be traveling through space in the alien ship. There is light coming toward you from one direction and you get up and walk toward it. Then you realize you are looking through the opening of your cave. You hurry out and, to your joy, find Snake Canyon just as you remembered it. You are back in your own time.

It's a long while before you feel like visiting Snake Canyon again. When you do, you find the opening to the Cave of Time has been covered over by a massive rock slide, and, you think to yourself that may be just as well.

The End

ABOUT THE AUTHOR

A graduate of Princeton University and Columbia Law School, *Edward Packard* lives in New York City, where he is a practicing lawyer. Mr. Packard conceived of the idea for the Choose Your Own Adventure ™ series in the course of telling bedtime stories to his children, Caroline, Andrea, and Wells.

ABOUT THE ILLUSTRATOR

Paul Granger is a prize-winning illustrator and painter.

You're the star of the story! Choose from 42 possible endings.

JOURNEY UNDER THE SEA

BY R. A. MONTGOMERY

You are the hero of a fabulous deep sea adventure

You are an underwater explorer. In the deepest ocean, you have accidentally been shut out of your special underwater vessel! Luckily you have friends above you in a boat. But can they save you in time? As they begin pulling you up, you get dizzy and your arms and legs start to feel weak ... you are exhausted! Then you see a dolphin heading toward you. You know that these marvelous mammals sometimes help people in trouble. *If you want help from the dolphin,* turn to p. 34. *If you decide to swim on alone,* turn to p. 37.

What happens next in the story? It all depends on the choices *you* make. How does the story end? Only you can find out! And the best part is that you can keep reading and rereading until you've had not *one*, but many incredibly daring experiences!

Choose your own adventure

0 553 14003 5   75p

You're the star of the story! Choose from 40 possible endings.

BY BALLOON TO THE SAHARA

BY D. TERMAN

What will happen on this exciting journey? You get to choose!

You are floating high above the earth in a giant balloon. Below you is the Sahara Desert, with its endless, golden sands, hundreds of camels, and mud-walled villages. Suddenly you see a large silver dome twinkling in the distance. Should you land the balloon and see what it is? If it's a flying saucer, it might be dangerous . . . should you play it safe and stay in the clouds?

If you decide to land, pull the cord and descend to p. 16.
If you decide to keep going, drift ahead to p. 17.

What happens next in the story? It all depends on the choices *you* make. How does the story end? Only you can find out! And the best part is that you can keep reading and re-reading until you've had not *one*, but *many* incredibly daring experiences!

Choose your own adventure

0 553 14005 1   75p

A SELECTED LIST OF
BOOKS PUBLISHED BY CORGI

WHILE EVERY EFFORT IS MADE TO KEEP PRICES LOW, IT IS SOMETIMES NECESSARY TO INCREASE PRICES AT SHORT NOTICE. CORGI BOOKS RESERVE THE RIGHT TO SHOW AND CHARGE NEW RETAIL PRICES ON COVERS WHICH MAY DIFFER FROM THOSE ADVERTISED IN THE TEXT OR ELSEWHERE.

THE PRICES SHOWN BELOW WERE CORRECT AT THE TIME OF GOING TO PRESS (JANUARY '82)

CHOOSE YOUR OWN ADVENTURE

☐ 20892 6	1: The Cave of Time	Edward Packard	75p
☐ 14003 5	2: Journey Under the Sea	R. A. Montgomery	75p
☐ 14005 1	3: By Balloon to the Sahara	D. Terman	75p
☐ 14000 0	4: Space and Beyond	R. A. Montgomery	75p
☐ 20961 2	5: The Mystery of Chimney Rock	Edward Packard	75p
☐ 14002 7	6: Your Code Name is Jonah	Edward Packard	75p

SWEET DREAMS

☐ 20323 1	P.S. I Love You (72)	Barbara Conklin	65p
☐ 20325 8	Popularity Plan (72)	Rosemary Vernon	65p
☐ 20327 4	Laurie's Song (72)	Suzanne Rand	65p
☐ 20328 2	Princess Amy (72)	Melinda Pollowitz	65p
☐ 20326 6	Little Sister (72)	Yvonne Greene	65p
☐ 20324 X	California Girl (72)	Jane Quin-Harkin	65p

All these books are available at your bookshop or newsagent, or can be ordered direct from the publisher. Just tick the titles you want and fill in the form below.

CORGI BOOKS, Cash Sales Department, P.O. Box 11, Falmouth, Cornwall.

Please send cheque or postal order, no currency.

Please allow cost of book(s) plus the following for postage and packing:

U.K. CUSTOMERS. 40p for the first book, 18p for the second book and 13p for each additional book ordered, to a maximum charge of £1.49.

B.F.P.O. & EIRE. Please allow 40p for the first book, 18p for the second book plus 13p per copy for the next three books, thereafter 7p per book.

OVERSEAS CUSTOMERS. Please allow 60p for the first book plus 18p per copy for each additional book.

NAME (Block letters)..

ADDRESS ....

....